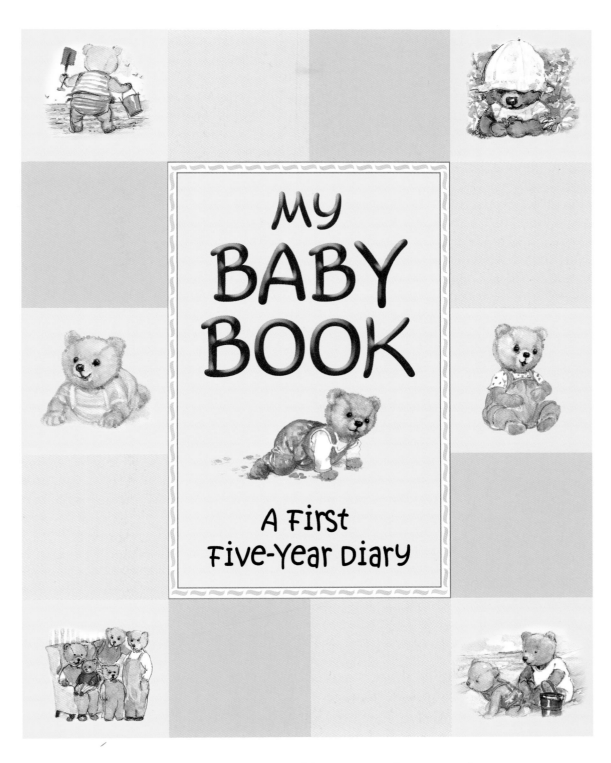

MY BABY BOOK

A First Five-Year Diary

Compiled and designed by Desmond Marwood

Illustrated by Patricia Ludlow

Brown Watson

ENGLAND

CONTENTS

Meet My Parents	3
My Arrival in this Funny Old World	4
My Family Tree	6
My Name	7
Register of My First Visitors	8
My Star Sign and Symbols	9
My First Presents	10
Arriving Home	11
First Days at Home	12
My Bedtimes	13
Getting Used to Water	14
My Early Playtimes	15
All About My Teeth	16
My Food and Drink	17
Getting on the Move	18
Some More of My First-Time Happenings	20
My First Haircut	22
My Favourite Toys	23
My Naming Day	24
Animals in My Life	25
Looking Back at My First Holiday	26
My Footprints and Handprints	28
My Weights and Measures	30
My Medical Records	31
My Four Favourite Friends	32
My First-Year Portrait Gallery	34
My First Birthday	36
My First Christmas	38
My Early Attempts to Paint and Draw	40
My Playgroup	42
More Happy Birthdays	43
My First Five Years of Special Happenings	44
My First Real School	46
My Early Schooldays	47
Bye-bye for Now!	48

First published 2001 by Brown Watson,
76 Fleckney Road, Kibworth, Leicester, LE8 0HG
© 2001 Brown Watson ISBN 978-0-7097-1382-1
Reprinted 2002 (twice), 2003 (twice), 2004 (twice), 2005 (thrice),
2006, 2007, 2008 (twice), 2009 (thrice), 2010, 2011 (thrice), 2012 (thrice), 2013 (twice), 2014 (twice), 2015, 2016, 2017

Meet My Parents

I was born about ....after this photograph was taken.

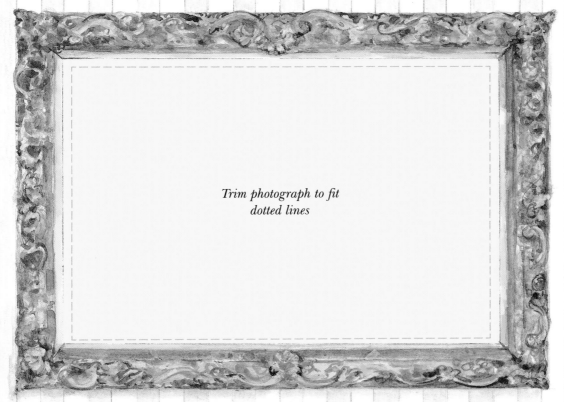

Trim photograph to fit dotted lines

Mother's name...........................

Father's name...........................

Mother's birthday is..../..../........

Father's birthday is..../..../.......

Mother's job was.........................

Father's job was.........................

This is a picture of my prenatal scan taken ...... weeks before I was even born!

Trim scan to fit dotted lines

5

My Arrival in this

My name is ....

....

....

....

I was born at (time)

....

I was born on (date)

....

My weight was.........................

My length was ....

My eyes were (colour) ....

My hair was (colour) ....

My Blood Group was ....

*Trim photograph to fit
dotted lines*

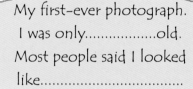

My first-ever photograph.
I was only.................old.
Most people said I looked
like...................................

Funny Old World

This is the place where I was born.
The address is....................................
....

The doctor's name was
....

The midwife's name was
....

Was my father present when
I arrived?.......................................

*Trim photograph to fit
dotted lines*

This is my hospital bracelet.

*Put the bracelet in a transparent
wrapper and fix here*

My Family Tree

Grandmother

Grandfather

Grandfather

Grandmother

Mother

Father

Me

My Sisters

My Brothers

My Name

My first name is

....

The country from which
this name comes is

....

What does this name mean?

....

....

....

Who chose my name?

....

Why was this name chosen?

....

....

My other first names are

....

Why were these names chosen?

....

....

Who chose these other names?

....

....

Register of My First Visitors

Signature	Printed Name	Relationship	Date	Time

My Star Sign and Symbols

My Birth Stone is ....

My Colour is ....

Aquarius

Pisces

Aries

Taurus

Gemini

Cancer

My Sign of the Zodiac is ....

My Birth Flower is ....

My Lucky Number is ....

My Chinese Horoscope symbol is ....

Leo

Virgo

Libra

Scorpio

Sagittarius

Capricorn

Monday's child is fair of face,
Tuesday's child is full of grace,
Wednesday's child is full of woe,
Thursday's child has far to go,
Friday's child is loving and giving,
Saturday's child works hard for its living,
And a child that's born on the Sabbath day
Is fair and wise and good at play.

My First Presents

BABY THOUGHT: Too late to worry about it now, but I hope my grown-ups sent them all nice thank you notes on my behalf!

Gift	From

10

Arriving Home

HOME,
SWEET HOME

This is a photograph of the first place in which I lived. It was my first home.

Trim photograph to fit dotted lines

The address was ....
....
....

I arrived at my first home on........./........./.............

I travelled there by...

I was wearing...

Where did I sleep in my new home? ....
....

I went to sleep at......... and woke at ....

I shared my home with.................................
....
....

Other comments about my first night at home!
....
....
....
....

First Days at Home

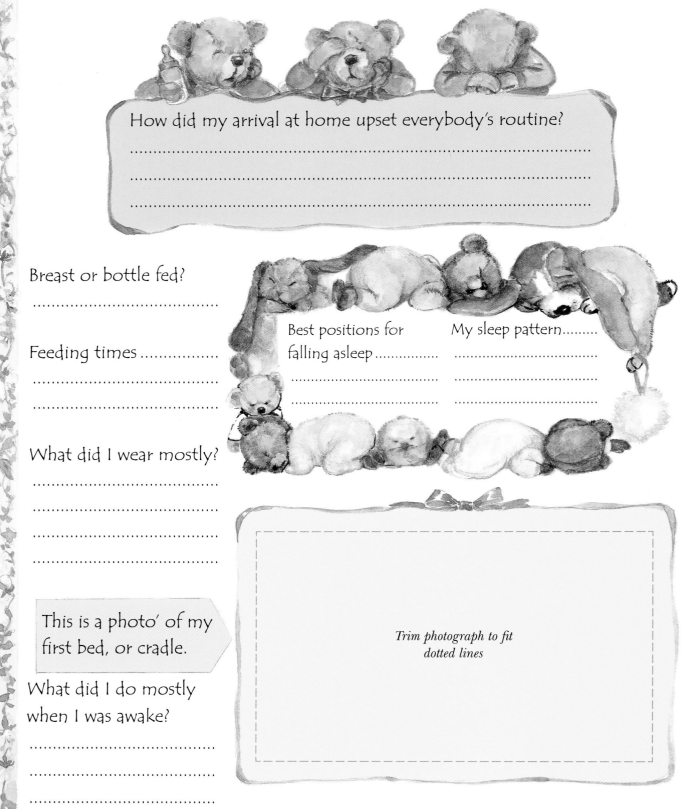

How did my arrival at home upset everybody's routine?

....
....
....

Breast or bottle fed?

....

Feeding times ....
....
....

What did I wear mostly?

....
....
....
....

Best positions for
falling asleep ....
....
....

My sleep pattern.........
....
....

This is a photo' of my
first bed, or cradle.

What did I do mostly
when I was awake?

....
....
....

*Trim photograph to fit
dotted lines*

My Bedtimes

My regular sleep pattern became.........hours until.........hours.

My first baby-sitter

Trim photograph to fit
dotted lines

Name and age of my
first baby-sitter ....
....
....

Relation or friend?
....
....

How old was I when I
had my first baby-sitter?
....
....

My favourite lullaby was
....

When was I moved
from a cradle to a cot?
....
....
....

This lullaby was usually
sung by ....

When did I first sleep
right through the night?
....
....

My favourite bedtime toy
was ....
....

The best way to send me
off to sleep was ....
....
....

Getting Used to Water

Did I like to make a splash?
....
....

Did I go into the big bath before I was one year old?
....

My favourite bath toys were ....
....
....

To begin with, did I like or dislike water? ....
....

Did I make a fuss about having my hair washed?
....
....

Did I like having my face wiped? ....
....

Did I enjoy bathtime?
....
....
....

My Early Playtimes

The first game I ever played that made me laugh was ....
....

How old was I when these games made me laugh?

Peek-a-boo.................................

Pulling funny faces.....................

Making funny noises.................

Being tossed in the air..............
....
Being danced around.................

Being tickled...............................

Playing with toys that squeaked or made a funny noise ....
....

Bouncing on the bed or on someone's knee.........................
....

All About My Teeth

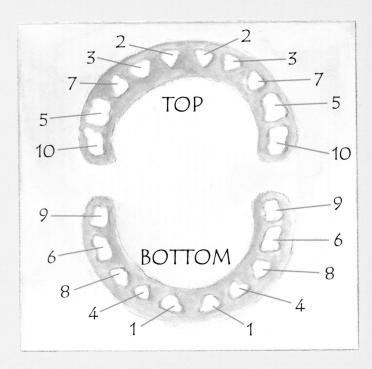

Growing or 'cutting' first teeth can be a painful time for babies. The first set of teeth which push up through our tender gums are called milk teeth.

Did I cry a lot when cutting my first teeth? ....

Most babies cut their two lower front teeth (1-1) at about the age of six months. How old was I when mine came through? ....

The two upper front teeth (2-2) appear at about the age of seven to nine months. How old was I when mine came through? ....

The upper side teeth (3-3) appear at about eight to nine months. How old was I when mine came through?...............

The lower side teeth (4-4) appear at about nine to ten months. How old was I when mine came through? ....

Did I have a teething ring to chew on to ease any pain?...

Did I have a dummy to comfort me?........

Did I have anything else to help get me through my teething problems?...............
....

The upper first molars (5-5) usually appear around a baby's first birthday. What age was I when mine came through?...

The rest of a baby's first teeth usually come through by the time they are 24 to 26 months old.

Lower first molars (6-6) appear at about 14 months (mine appeared at..............).

Upper eye teeth (7-7) appear at about 16 months (mine appeared at...................).

Lower eye teeth (8-8) appear at about 18 months (mine appeared at..............).

Lower second molars (9-9) appear at about 22-24 months (mine appeared at ....).

Upper second molars (10-10) appear at about 24-26 months (mine appeared at ....).

My Food and Drink

Here are some of my
least favourite foods.

....
....
....
....

Here are some of my
favourite baby foods.

....
....
....
....

Where did I usually
sit to eat my meals?

....
....

MENU		
Food or Drink	Date	Age
I was weaned from breast or bottle		
I had my first sip of tea		
I had my first sip of coffee		
I had my first drink of orange juice		
I first ate fruit		
I first ate puréed food		
What was it?		
I first ate solid food		
What was it?		
I ate chopped foods		
I began to feed myself		
I had my first ice-cream		
I ate my first piece of chocolate		
I first drank from a beaker or cup		

Getting on

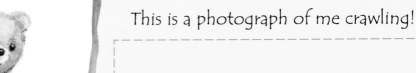

On ...../...../.....
I rolled over onto
my back and then rolled right over back onto my tummy on ...../...../.....

I began
to sit up
by myself
on ...../...../.....

This is a photograph of me crawling!

*Trim photograph to fit
dotted lines*

Finally, I started to walk!

I began
to shuffle on
my bottom
on ...../...../.....

*Trim photograph to fit
dotted lines*

I began
to crawl
on all fours
on ...../...../.....

Photograph of me taking some early steps.
I took my very first steps on ...../...../.....

the Move

OUT OF DOORS

Later, I was taken for walks in a pram!

*Trim photograph to fit
dotted lines*

This is me being taken for a walk in my pram. I was ....months old and......................was pushing my pram. Also with us was.........
....
....
The photograph was taken by
....

When I first went outside I was lifted in and out of the car in a carrycot.

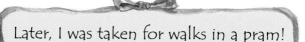

Here I am again wearing reins to help me take my first steps out of doors. I was .... months old.

*Trim photograph to fit
dotted lines*

Sometimes I was taken to feed the ducks on the pond.

My first time in the RAIN...

Trim photograph to fit dotted lines

Here's a photograph of me with ....
....
....
It was taken at......................
...............on....../....../.....

My first time in the SUN...

Trim photograph to fit dotted lines

Here's a photograph of me with ....
....
....
It was taken at......................
...............on....../....../.....

My first time in the SNOW...
Here's a photograph of me with ....
....
....
It was taken at......................
...............on....../....../.....

Trim photograph to fit dotted lines

First-Time Happenings

WEARING SOME OF MY FIRST REAL CLOTHES...

Trim photograph to fit dotted lines

Trim photograph to fit dotted lines

Trim photograph to fit dotted lines

My first shoes!
I was.................
months old.

My first gloves!
I was.................
months old.

My first hat!
I was.................
months old.

SOME OF MY FIRST WORDS...

What I said...	When I said it...	How old I was...
Mum or Mummy	..../..../....	
Dad or Daddy	..../..../....	
Grandpa' or Grandad	..../..../....	
Grandma' or Nan	..../..../....	
Dog	..../..../....	
Cat	..../..../....	

My other favourite early words were...

My First Haircut

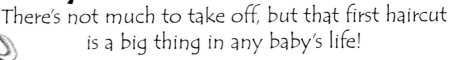

There's not much to take off, but that first haircut
is a big thing in any baby's life!

BEFORE my haircut	DURING my haircut	AFTER my haircut
Trim photograph to fit dotted lines	*Trim photograph to fit dotted lines*	*Trim photograph to fit dotted lines*

Here is a lock of hair from my first haircut.

Place the lock of hair in a transparent sealed envelope and fix into this area

Comments from others about my first haircut...................................
....
....
....

My Favourite Toys

ME with my favourite
BEDTIME toy

*Trim photograph to fit
dotted lines*

It was a ....
called ....

ME with my favourite
BATHTIME toy

*Trim photograph to fit
dotted lines*

It was a ....
called ....

ME with my most favourite
toy I took almost
EVERYWHERE I went!

*Trim photograph to fit
dotted lines*

It was a ....
called ....

Guess what my
favourite toy was to
take OUT IN THE CAR!

It was a ....called ....

23

My Naming Day

This is a very special day when family and friends gather together to celebrate the arrival of a baby into their lives and officially record its name.
The Naming Ceremony itself is usually held in a place of worship and conducted by a leader of a religious faith.

Some of the guests at my Naming Day

This is a picture of me on my Naming Day.
I am being held by ....
....
....
....

Trim photograph to fit dotted lines

My Naming Day took place at...................
....

My Naming Day was on ....../....../.....

I was named (see My Name on Page 7)
....
....

How did I behave?.......................................
....
....
....

I was...................old at the time.

I was wearing ....

The ceremony itself was performed by (e.g .representative of appropriate faith)
....

My godparents (if any were appointed) were...
....
....

Animals in My Life

This is ME with (enter pet name)
....
(Pet name) ....
is a ....

*Trim photograph to fit
dotted lines*

(Pet name) ....
belongs to...
(Pet name) ....
lives in ....

This is ME with (enter pet name)
....
(Pet name) ....
is a ....

*Trim photograph to fit
dotted lines*

(Pet name) ....
belongs to...
(Pet name) ....
lives in ....

This is ME with (enter pet name)
....
(Pet name) ....
is a ....

*Trim photograph to fit
dotted lines*

(Pet name) ....
belongs to...
(Pet name) ....
lives in ....

25

Looking Back at

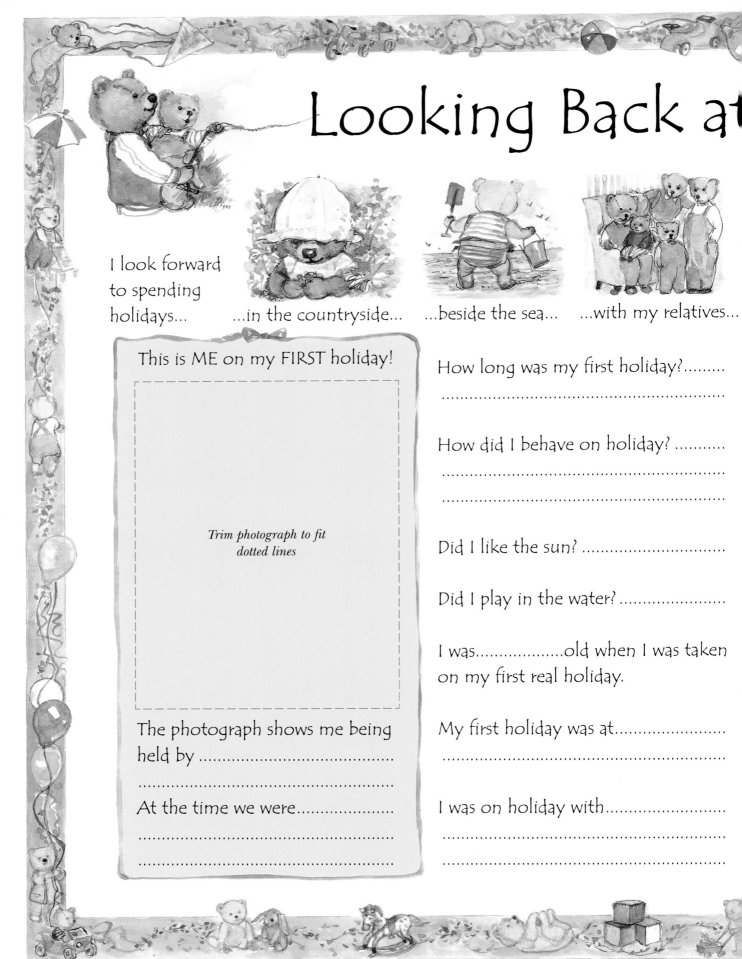

I look forward to spending holidays...

...in the countryside...

...beside the sea...

...with my relatives...

This is ME on my FIRST holiday!

Trim photograph to fit dotted lines

The photograph shows me being held by ....

....

At the time we were.....................

....

....

How long was my first holiday?.........

....

How did I behave on holiday? ....

....

....

Did I like the sun? ....

Did I play in the water? ....

I was....................old when I was taken on my first real holiday.

My first holiday was at.......................

....

I was on holiday with..........................

....

....

My First Holiday

Here are more photographs of ME on my FIRST HOLIDAY!

*Trim photographs
to make a display
within this area*

They show...

....

The weather was
(tick the box)...

 sunny

 rainy

 windy

 snowy

We travelled by
(tick the box)...

 car

 train

 bus

 boat

 aircraft

We stayed in a
(tick the box)...

 hotel

 caravan

 apartment

 tent

 house

27

My Footprints

MY FOOTPRINTS

*Trim the photograph
of my feet to fit
into this area.
Arrange my footprints
in the spaces at the sides.*

At the time I was ....old.

IMPORTANT ADVICE!

It is essential to choose a non-toxic paint to cover the soles of baby's feet and the palms of its hands. Wipe off any surplus paint before gently pressing the hands and feet in turn wherever the prints are to appear. To make sure there is just the right amount of paint on baby's feet and hands, it is advisable to practise on a piece of paper before attempting to print them in this book.

CLEANLINESS AFTERWARDS!
It is essential that, after you have taken the prints, baby's feet and particularly hands are thoroughly washed and free from paint!

nd Handprints

MY HANDPRINTS

*Trim the photograph
of my hands to fit
into this area.
Arrange my handprints
in the spaces at the sides.*

At the time I was ....old.

Baby's handprints and footprints can also be used to decorate the surround to a photograph. Pop the whole thing in a frame and make an unusual wall picture to treasure!

My Weights and Measures

Growing taller all the time...

...from the early days...

...when I was first...

...measured at birth!

RECORD OF MY FIRST TWELVE MONTHS

Date	Age (months)	Weight (kilograms)	Height (centimetres)
...../...../.....			
...../...../.....			
...../...../.....			
...../...../.....			
...../...../.....			
...../...../.....			
...../...../.....			
...../...../.....			
...../...../.....			
...../...../.....			
...../...../.....			
...../...../.....			

My Medical Records

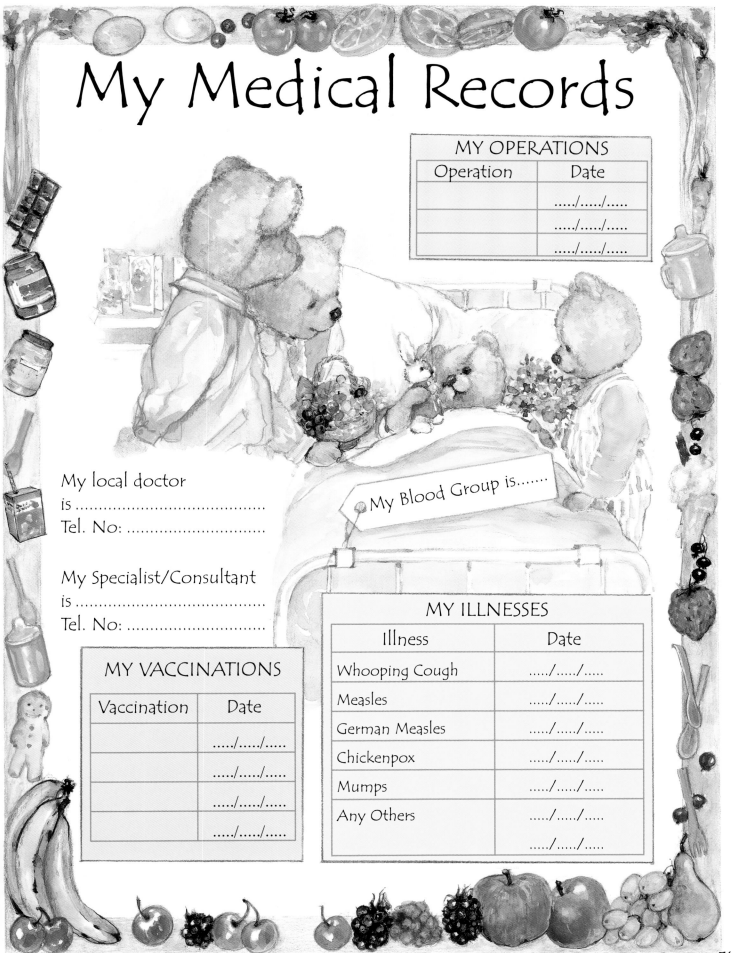

MY OPERATIONS

Operation	Date
	...../...../.....
	...../...../.....
	...../...../.....

My local doctor
is ....
Tel. No: ....

My Specialist/Consultant
is ....
Tel. No: ....

My Blood Group is.......

MY VACCINATIONS

Vaccination	Date
	...../...../.....
	...../...../.....
	...../...../.....
	...../...../.....

MY ILLNESSES

Illness	Date
Whooping Cough	...../...../.....
Measles	...../...../.....
German Measles	...../...../.....
Chickenpox	...../...../.....
Mumps	...../...../.....
Any Others	...../...../.....
	...../...../.....

This is my friend.....................
....
My friend is.....................old.

Here are my four favourite friends.
We meet at parties, sometimes
out shopping, at the playgroup or just
out and about. We have great fun
playing together.

*Trim photograph to fit
dotted lines*

We met at..............................
....
The photograph shows...........
....
....

This is my friend.....................
....
My friend is.....................old.

*Trim photograph to fit
dotted lines*

We met at..............................
....
The photograph shows...........
....
....

avourite Friends

This is my friend.....................
....
My friend is.....................old.

Trim photograph to fit dotted lines

We met at.................................
....
The photograph shows............
....
....

This is my friend.....................
....
My friend is.....................old.

Trim photograph to fit dotted lines

We met at.................................
....
The photograph shows............
....
....

My First-Yea

ME at ONE MONTH

Trim photograph to fit dotted lines

ME at TWO MONTHS

Trim photograph to fit dotted lines

ME at THREE MONTHS

Trim photograph to fit dotted lines

ME at FOUR MONTHS

Trim photograph to fit dotted lines

ME at SIX MONTHS

Trim photograph to fit dotted lines

ME at FIVE MONTHS

Trim photograph to fit dotted lines

Portrait Gallery

ME at SEVEN MONTHS

Trim photograph to fit dotted lines

ME at EIGHT MONTHS

Trim photograph to fit dotted lines

ME at NINE MONTHS

Trim photograph to fit dotted lines

ME at TEN MONTHS

Trim photograph to fit dotted lines

ME at ELEVEN MONTHS

Trim photograph to fit dotted lines

ME at TWELVE MONTHS

Trim photograph to fit dotted lines

My Firs

*Trim photograph to fit
dotted lines*

BIRTHDAY GUESTS
Photo' shows some of
my visitors on that very
special day. They were

....
....
....
....
....
....

Birthday

Happy Birthday to ME!
Happy Birthday to ME!
Happy Birthday DEAR BABY,
Happy Birthday to ME!

PHOTOGRAPH
OF ME AGED
ONE YEAR

*Trim photograph to fit
dotted lines*

I weighed................

I was...............long.

SOME OF MY PRESENTS...

Name of Sender	Type of Gift

Members of many religions are now able to join in the celebration of Christmas. It has become more than solely a period for the Christian commemoration of the birth of Jesus Christ, the son of their Lord God.

For those who so wish, it has become a season of fun, parties and the exchange of gifts, greeting cards and goodwill between all people on Earth.

My First

CHRISTMAS EVE

This is the night before Christmas Day. We hang up our stockings before going to bed. We hope Santa Claus will put presents in them for us during the night.

Trim photograph to fit dotted lines

Photograph shows ME about to hang up my stocking before going to bed.

CHRISTMAS DAY

Christmas Day is on 25 December every year.

Trim photograph to fit dotted lines

Photograph shows ME on my first Christmas Day which was 25 December, 20......

On my first Christmas Day, I was........................old.

MY CHRISTMAS GIFTS

I cannot remember how many I received, but grown-ups tell me that altogether I had about..........presents.

One of my favourite presents was a toy...........................that we called by the name of................................. It was a present from...

Christmas

DURING MY FIRST CHRISTMAS...

Tick...	Yes	No
I ate Christmas Cake		
I ate Christmas Pudding		
I pulled a Christmas Cracker		
I ate turkey, chicken, duck or pork?		
I ate mince pies		
I ate jelly		
I ate trifle		
I ate ice-cream		
What did I most enjoy eating?		
What did I drink?		

GROWN-UPS SAID I...............

....

....

....

....

....

SANTA CLAUS

Santa Claus is the person who many believe brings gifts to people at Christmas.

Photograph shows ME with Santa Claus at.................................

....

Trim photograph to fit dotted lines

My Early Attempt

PENCIL AND CRAYON

NOTE TO GROWN-UPS!
To avoid spoiling the book, while preserving this great piece of art, please take care not to close the book until the water colours are completely dry.

I produced this masterpiece on....../....../......
I was................old at the time.

It was supposed to be a picture of
....
....

:o Paint and Draw

WATER COLOUR PAINTS

SAVE THE PAINTING!
It may be worth a
lot of money if I ever
become famous!

I produced this masterpiece on....../....../......
I was................old at the time

It was supposed to
be a picture of

....

....

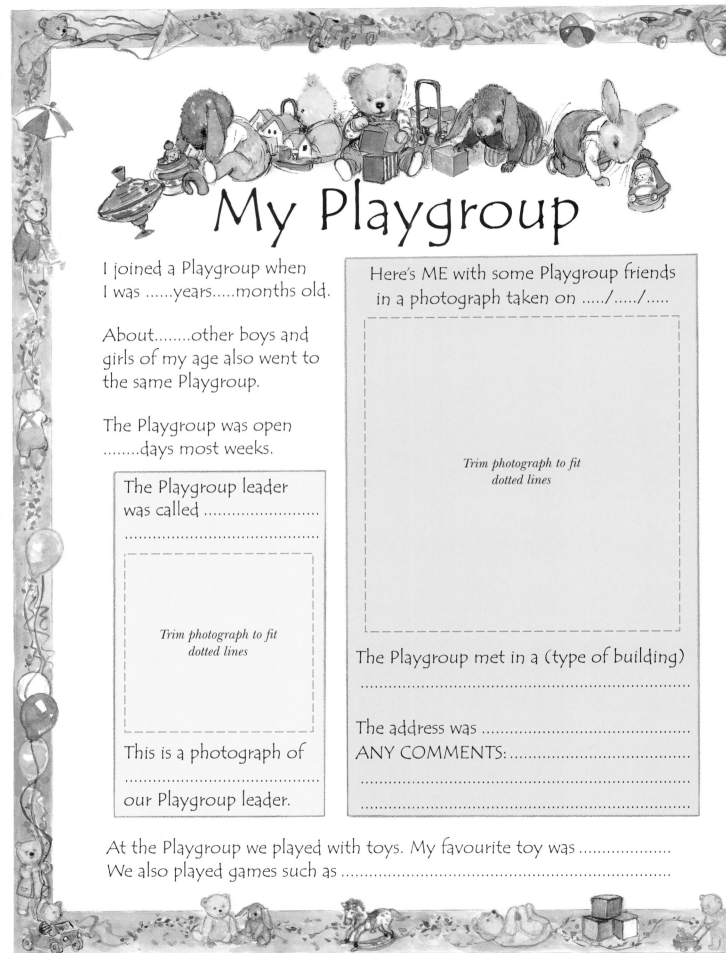

My Playgroup

I joined a Playgroup when I was ......years.....months old.

About........other boys and girls of my age also went to the same Playgroup.

The Playgroup was open ....days most weeks.

The Playgroup leader was called ....
....

Trim photograph to fit dotted lines

This is a photograph of
....
our Playgroup leader.

Here's ME with some Playgroup friends in a photograph taken on ...../...../.....

Trim photograph to fit dotted lines

The Playgroup met in a (type of building)
....

The address was ....
ANY COMMENTS:...
....
....

At the Playgroup we played with toys. My favourite toy was ....
We also played games such as ....

More Happy Birthdays

1 Year Old

Trim photograph of ME to fit in this area

My Height.............
My Weight...........

2 Years Old

Trim photograph of ME to fit in this area

My Height.............
My Weight...........

3 Years Old

Trim photograph of ME to fit in this area

My Height.............
My Weight...........

4 Years Old

Trim photograph of ME to fit in this area

My Height.............
My Weight...........

5 Years Old

Trim photograph of ME to fit in this area

My Height.............
My Weight...........

Save one photograph of me every year to complete this page of portrait pictures. See if I have changed very much during my early growing-up years!

My First Five Year

A record of some of the special moments in my young life so far!

Trim photograph to fit dotted lines

I was aged..........when
....
....
....
....
....

Trim photograph to fit dotted lines

I was aged..........when
....
....
....
....
....

Trim photograph to fit dotted lines

I was aged..........when........................
....
....

Trim photograph to fit
dotted lines

I was aged..........when

....
....
....

Trim photograph to fit
dotted lines

I was aged..........when

....
....
....

Trim photograph to fit
dotted lines

I was aged..........when

....
....
....
....

Trim photograph to fit
dotted lines

I was aged..........when..............................

....
....
....

My First Real School

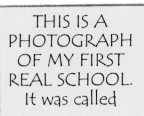

THIS IS A PHOTOGRAPH OF MY FIRST REAL SCHOOL.
It was called
....
....

The address was
....
....

Trim photograph to fit dotted lines

I went to my first real school when I was just ....old.

It was on ...../...../.....

I was taken to school by ....

How did we travel to school that day? ....
....

THIS IS A PHOTOGRAPH OF MY TEACHER

Trim photograph to fit dotted lines

My teacher's name was ....
....

How did I behave on my first day at school?
....
....
....
....
....
....
....
....
....

My Early Schooldays

THIS IS MY FIRST SCHOOL CLASS PHOTOGRAPH

*Trim photograph to fit
dotted lines*

I was..........old at the time. You can see me in the ....row,
..........in from the ....

My favourite lesson was.........................

My favourite game at school was ....

My worst lesson was ....

I was good at..........

Did I like or dislike school?...........................

Bye-bye for Now!

THANKS TO EVERYONE FOR MY WONDERFUL WORLD!

*Trim photograph to fit
dotted lines*

I am now five years old. In this photograph are other members of my family. They include ....

....

....

....

Here's looking forward to the next five years!